AGE

7–8

Year 3

FOR THE YEAR **2004**

Maths and English
Optional Tests Levels 2–4

practice
papers

Acknowledgements

The authors and publisher would like to thank the following for permission to reproduce material in this book.

A Spike of Green by Barbara Baker, from *Shades of Green* (ed. Ann Harvey), Red Fox 1993

First published 2003
exclusively for WHSmith by
Hodder & Stoughton Educational
a division of Hodder Headline Ltd
338 Euston Road
London NW1 3BH

A CIP record for this book is available from the British Library.

Authors: Steve Mills and Hilary Koll (Maths);
Christine Moorcroft and Ray Barker (English)

ISBN 0340 81391 1

Impression   5 4 3 2 1
Year   2004 2003

Printed and bound by Hobbs The Printers, Totton, Hampshire.

NOTE: The tests, questions and advice in this book are not reproductions of the official test materials sent to schools. The official testing process is supported by guidance and training for teachers in setting and marking tests and interpreting the results. The results achieved in the tests in this book may not be the same as are achieved in the official tests.

The National Tests: A Summary

What are the National Tests?

Children who attend state schools in England and Wales sit National Tests (also known as SATs) at the ages of 7, 11 and 14, usually at the beginning of May. They may also sit optional tests in the intervening years – many schools have chosen to adopt these tests. The test results are accompanied by an assessment by the child's teacher (at Key Stage 3 this also covers non-tested subjects such as History or Geography).

The results are used by the school to assess each child's level of knowledge and progress in English and Maths at Key Stage 1 and English, Maths and Science at Key Stages 2 and 3. They also provide useful guidance for the child's next teacher when he or she is planning the year's work.

The educational calendar for children aged 5–14 is structured as follows:

Key Stage	Year	Age by end of year	National Test
1 (KS1)	1	6	
	2	7	KEY STAGE 1
2 (KS2)	3	8	Optional Year 3
	4	9	Optional Year 4
	5	10	Optional Year 5
	6	11	KEY STAGE 2
3 (KS3)	7	12	Optional Year 7
	8	13	Optional Year 8
	9	14	KEY STAGE 3

Test timetable

The Key Stage 1 National Tests are carried out in **May**. They often form part of the children's normal school day, as they are generally practical and teacher-assessed. Many children at Key Stage 1 do not even realise they are taking a test.

Key Stage 2 tests take place in one week in May. All children sit the same test at the same time. In 2004, the tests will take place in the week of **10–14 May**. Your child's school will be able to provide you with a detailed timetable.

Key Stage 3 students will sit their tests on **4–7 May**.

Levels

National average levels have been set for children's results in the National Tests. The levels are as follows:

LEVEL	AGE 7 (Key Stage 1)	AGE 11 (Key Stage 2)	AGE 14 (Key Stage 3)
8			
7			
6			
5			
4			
3			
2			
2a			
2b			
2c			
1			

- **BELOW EXPECTED LEVEL**
- **EXPECTED LEVEL**
- **ABOVE EXPECTED LEVEL**
- **EXCEPTIONAL**

Results

Your child's school will send you a report including his or her levels in the tests and the teacher assessment.

The school's overall test results will be included in local and national league tables, which are published in most newspapers.

What can parents do to help?

While it is never a good idea to encourage cramming, you can help your child to succeed by:

- making sure he or she has enough food, sleep and leisure time during the test period
- practising important skills such as writing and reading stories, spelling and mental arithmetic
- telling him or her what to expect in the test, such as important symbols and key words
- helping him or her to be comfortable in test conditions including working within a time limit, reading questions carefully and understanding different ways of answering.

Maths at Year 3

Typical seven-year-olds attain Level 2 in Maths at the end of Year 2. By the end of Year 3 most children will have achieved Level 2 and be working towards Level 3. Some might be attaining a Level 3 and some very able children might attain Level 4.

Setting the test

The written test

The written test is split into two parts, A and B. If your child scores highly in Part A, he or she can go on to try the harder questions in Part B. There is not a strict time limit on this test, but do not force your child to continue if he or she can no longer answer any questions.

Allow between 45 minutes and one hour to complete the written test. If your child attempts Part B allow longer.

Your child will need a ruler, pencil, rubber, and, if possible, a small mirror or piece of tracing paper. No extra writing paper is needed. The use of a calculator is not permitted.

If your child has difficulty in reading the questions, these can be read aloud, provided the mathematical words are not altered or explained. Where necessary, children can dictate their answers for you to write them down. For large numbers, however, a child should be clear which digits are intended to be written, e.g. for a number such as three thousand and six the child must indicate that this should be written three, zero, zero, six.

The mental test

The marks scored on the mental arithmetic test are not included when levelling at Year 3. However, in the Year 6 National Tests your child's mental scores will form part of the overall mark used for levelling.

The mental test should take approximately 10–15 minutes to give, and it is necessary for you to read aloud the questions on pages 17 and 18. Cut this page out for this purpose. Your child will only need a pencil and rubber for the mental test.

The mental test contains a series of questions for you to read to your child and answer sheets for him or her to write answers on. Allow only the time suggested for each question and read each question twice.

Marking the test

Next to each question in the written test is a number indicating how many marks the question or part of the question is worth. Enter your child's mark into the circle, using the answer pages to help you decide how many points to award.

Find your child's total score from the written test and refer to page 26 for information about the level your child might be working at.

1 Write a number in the circle to make this correct.

$$12 + 9 = 30 - \bigcirc$$

2 Alice has some coins.

TOTAL

How much money has she in total?

               P

3 Complete this pattern.

| 36 | 39 | | 45 | | |

4 Draw the next face in the pattern.

5 Which number is exactly halfway between 50 and 100?

Write the number in the box.

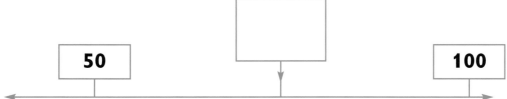

50   100

TOTAL

3

6 Draw the reflection of this pattern. You can use a mirror.

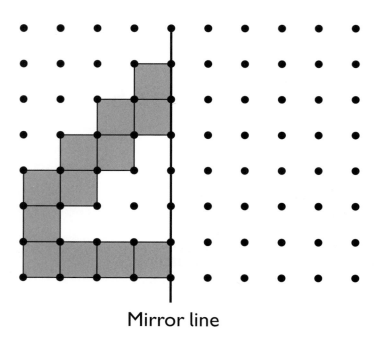

Mirror line

7 Fill in the missing numbers.

a $24 + \triangle = 41$

b $62 - \diamond = 57$

8 Count back in ones from 211.

| 211 | 210 | | | | |

TOTAL

4

9   Draw a line with a ruler that is **twice as long** as this line.

_____

10   Use these digits to make some **three-digit** numbers.

| 5 | 8 | 1 |

a   Write the largest **three-digit** number.

b   Write the smallest **three-digit** number.

c   Write an **even** number.

d   Write a number between 400 and 700.

1

1

1

1

1

TOTAL

5

5

11 Fill in the missing numbers.

1

a   35 ÷  = 7

1

b   ⬭ × 3 = 24

12 Draw a ring around **all** the **multiples** of 5.

1

24   35   40   76   90

100   165   217   450   152

13 This table shows the number of letters the postman delivered to each house in Back Lane.

1

House number	Number of letters
1	6
2	7
3	4
4	5
5	2

How many more letters did house number 2 get than house number 5?

TOTAL

4

14 Look at these cards.

Use these cards to make correct number sentences.

You can use each card more than once.

a 35 ☐ 7 ☐ 5

b 3 ☐ 3 ☐ 1

1

1

15 The time now is shown here.

(7 : 40)

A train leaves in half an hour.

What time does the train leave?

(:)

1

16 Round these numbers to the nearest ten by drawing a line to the correct circle.

38   52   31   47   43   29

(30)   (40)   (50)

1

TOTAL

4

7

17 What is the mass of the potatoes?

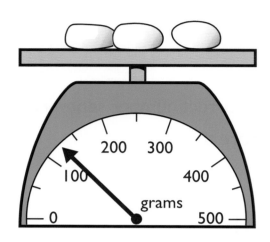

g

18 Four lengths of string, each **20 cm** long, are cut from a **2 m** ball of string.

Which of these would you use to find how much string is left on the ball?

4 + 20 + 2   4 x 20 + 200

200 – 80   80 + 2

200 – (4 × 20)   2 – (4 × 20)

19 Some children made a bar chart to show how far they could throw a beanbag.

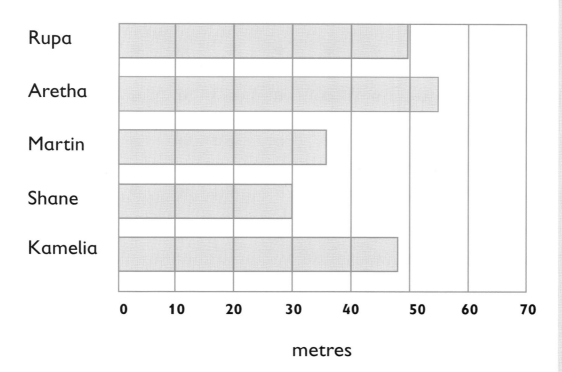

Rupa

Aretha

Martin

Shane

Kamelia

0   10   20   30   40   50   60   70

metres

a Estimate how far Martin threw the beanbag.

1

b Estimate how much further Aretha threw the beanbag than Shane did.

1

c Which children threw the beanbag further than 45 metres?

1

TOTAL

3

9

20 Use a ruler to join dots to draw a **hexagon** that is **not symmetrical**.

2

21 Estimate the number of cubes used to make this shape.

1

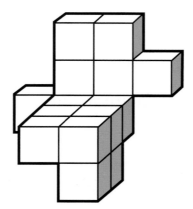

Tick the best estimate from this list.

Between 10 and 13   Between 14 and 17

Between 18 and 22   Between 23 and 28

TOTAL

3

STOP HERE AND MARK THE TEST

22 Find the **total** of **46** and **28**.

Show your working in this box.

1

23 Find the **difference** between **91** and **38**.

Show your working in this box.

1

24 Write the number that is exactly **halfway** between

 and

1

TOTAL

3

25 a + b Fill in the missing spaces of this **tally chart**.

Number of cubes some children can hold in one hand

Name	Tally	Number of cubes
Jamie	卌 ‖	7
Alex	卌 卌 |	11
Jennifer		9
Chloe	卌 ‖‖	
Rakeeb		12

This information has been drawn onto a graph.

One child's information has been wrongly drawn onto the graph.

c Write the name of this child.

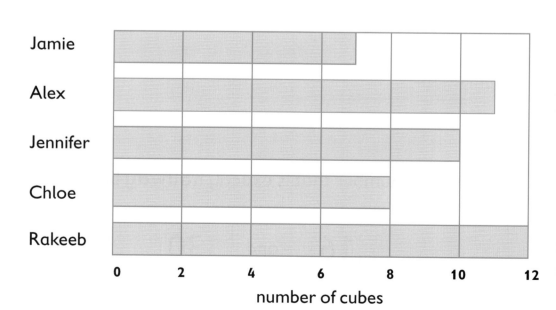

number of cubes

2

1

26 506 + 295 = ?

Show your working in this box.

1

27 How much water is there in the jug?

ml

1

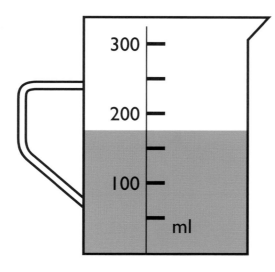

300 —

200 —

100 —

ml

28 Multiply 32 by 5.

Show your working in this box.

1

TOTAL

3

13

1

29 Draw a ring around the **three** numbers that when **divided by 2** leave no remainder.

$$27 \qquad 50 \qquad 104 \qquad 79 \qquad 198$$

1

30 $906 - 245 = ?$

Show your working in this box.

1

31 What is the **perimeter** of this shape?

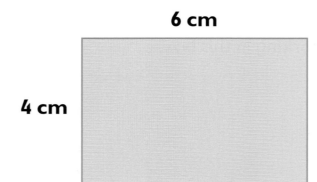

6 cm

4 cm

TOTAL

3

14

32 Write these decimals in order in the circles, starting with the largest.

3.7   8.1   0.9   25.2   3.5

largest

smallest

1

33 Circle **two** fractions below that are equivalent.

$\frac{1}{8}$ $\frac{2}{3}$ $\frac{2}{10}$ $\frac{3}{4}$

$\frac{1}{5}$ $\frac{4}{5}$ $\frac{1}{4}$

1

TOTAL

2

34

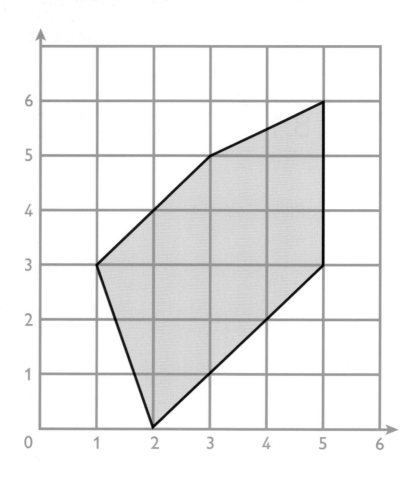

Here are the co-ordinates of three of the corners of this shape.

(1, 3)   (5, 3)   (3, 5)

Write the co-ordinates of the other two corners of this shape.

(,)   (,)

1

TOTAL

1

"For this first set of questions you have five seconds to work out each answer and write it down."

1   What is double eight?

2   What is ten more than thirty-five?

3   What is five multiplied by eight?

4   Add nineteen to fifteen.

5   Write the number two hundred and four in figures.

6   Jamie has a two pound coin. He spends one pound thirty. How much does he have now?

7   Subtract twenty-one from one hundred.

8   Jo put on a video at midday. It lasted three quarters of an hour. What time did it finish?

9   An arrow is facing North. It turns anticlockwise through one right angle. Which direction is the arrow facing now?

10   There are thirty-two children in a class. Nineteen are girls. How many are boys?

11   Divide sixty by fifteen.

12   What is three pounds twenty plus two pounds forty?

"For the next set of questions you have ten seconds to work out each answer and write it down."

13 Look at the answer sheet. Tick the shape that has exactly one right angle.

14 Look at the answer sheet. Which of these temperatures is the coldest?

15 What is the cost of four pens at fifty pence each?

16 Look at the answer sheet. If sixteen marbles fit into the first box, estimate how many marbles would fit into the second box.

17 What number is one-quarter of thirty-two?

18 If two hundred sweets are shared equally between five people, how many sweets does each person get?

19 Look at the answer sheet. Circle the decimal that is equivalent to one-tenth.

20 I'm thinking of a number. I subtract twenty-five from it. My answer is seventy. What is my number?

Five-second questions

1 _____

2 _____

3 _____

4 _____ 19   15

5 _____

6 _____

7 _____

8 _____

N

↑

9 _____

10 _____ 32 children

11 _____

12 _____

1
1
1
1
1
1
1
1
1
1
1
1
TOTAL

12

19

Ten-second questions

13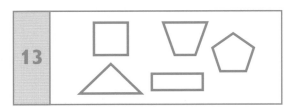

14
$$15°C$$
$$-1°C \qquad 0°C$$
$$-\frac{1}{2}°C$$
$$-7°C$$
$$-5°C$$

15 £

16

17

18

19   1.0   1.1   10.0   0.1

20

1

1

1

1

1

1

1

1

TOTAL

8

20

Question number	Answer	Mark	Parent's notes and additional information
Part A			
1	12 +9 = 30 – ⑨	1	Children sometimes make mistakes with this type of question as they do not fully understand the meaning of the equals sign (=). Some children incorrectly view it as an 'answer giver' and will say that 12 + 9 does not give the answer 30. Show your child that the equals sign stands for 'is the same value as', to demonstrate that the answer to one side of the number sentence is the same as the answer to the other side.
2	73p	1	
3	36, 39, **42**, 45, **48**, **51**	1	Ask your child to explain in words what the pattern is, e.g. it is going up in threes, or that it goes even, odd, even, odd etc.
4		1	Children should be able to describe this turn as a quarter turn or a turn through one right angle.
5	75	1	
6		1	Children can use a mirror or tracing paper for this question.
7a	17	1	
7b	5	1	
8	211, 210, 209, 208, 207, 206, 205, 204, 203, 202, 201, 200, 199	1	Ask your child to read each number aloud to ensure they can read the numerals correctly.
9	A line that is 12 cm long	1	Allow up to 2 mm for error.
10a	851	1	Use number cards to practise. Give your child several cards and ask him or her to make two- or three-digit numbers greater (more) than or less than a given number, or lying between two. Ask him or her to make odd or even numbers or those divisible by 2, 5 or 10.

Question number	Answer	Mark	Parent's notes and additional information
10b	158	1	
10c	158 or 518	1	
10d	518 or 581	1	
11a	5	1	
11b	8	1	
12	35, 40 ,90, 100, 165, 450 All the numbers above must be circled for a point to be awarded.	1	A multiple is a number that can be exactly divided by another with no remainder. Some children incorrectly think that multiples of a number, e.g. 5, are limited to the answers of that times table, e.g. 5, 10, 15 … up to 50. Ensure your child realises that multiples of a number continue beyond the range of a times table.
13	5	1	
14a	$35 \div 7 = 5$ *or* $35 = 7 \times 5$	1	
14b	$3 \div 3 = 1$ *or* $3 = 3 \times 1$	1	
15	8:10	1	Discuss the different ways of showing or describing the times on a clock, e.g. 7:40 can be described as 'seven forty', 'twenty to eight', 'twenty minutes to eight' etc. and can be shown on a traditional clock face or in digital form.
16	38 52 31 47 43 29 30 40 50 Two numbers will be joined to each of the multiples of 10.	1	If children find this difficult, show them these numbers on a number line and ask them to see which multiple of ten is closer.
17	125 g	1	As there are two sections between 100 and 200, each section must stand for 50, therefore halfway between 100 and 150 is 125.
18	$200 - 80$ *or* $200 - (4 \times 20)$	1	
19a	36 m	1	
19b	25 m	1	
19c	Kamelia, Rupa and Aretha	1	

Question number	Answer	Mark	Parent's notes and additional information
20	A six-sided shape with no lines of reflective symmetry, e.g.	2	Encourage children to use a mirror to check for lines of symmetry. Award 1 mark if a six-sided shape has been drawn that <u>has</u> one or more lines of symmetry.
21	Between 14 and 17	1	
Part B			
22	74	1	Any non-calculator method can be used to find the answer.
23	53	1	The mathematical word *difference* means subtracting the smaller number from the larger number.
24	23	1	A useful way of finding the number halfway between two others is to add the two numbers, e.g. 16 and 30, and then halve the answer, e.g. $46 \div 2 = 23$.
25a	1 mark for both correct tallies, i.e. 卌 IIII and 卌 卌 II	1	
25b	8	1	
25c	Jennifer	1	The graph shows incorrectly that Jennifer can hold 10 cubes in her hand, rather than 9.
26	801	1	Any non-calculator method can be used to find the answer.
27	175 ml	1	
28	160	1	Any non-calculator method can be used to find the answer. A useful mental strategy for multiplying by 5 is to multiply by 10 and halve, e.g. $32 \times 5 =$ half (32×10).
29	50, 104, 198	1	
30	661	1	Any non-calculator method can be used to find the answer.

Maths Test Answers

Question number	Answer	Mark	Parent's notes and additional information
31	20 cm	1	The perimeter of a shape is the distance all the way around the edge.
32	25.2, 8.1, 3.7, 3.5, 0.9	1	Encourage your child to cross each number off the list as he or she writes them in the circles.
33	$\frac{2}{10}$ and $\frac{1}{5}$	1	Equivalent means that the fractions have the same value, e.g. $\frac{2}{10}$ of a cake is the same value as $\frac{1}{5}$ of the cake.
34	(2, 0), (5, 6)	1	Remind your child that the first co-ordinate tells you how many across and the second tells you how many up (or down). Use the phrase 'Into the house and up the stairs' to help children remember the order.

Award 1 mark per correct answer.

1. 16

2. 45

3. 40

4. 34

5. 204 (do not accept this in words)

6. 70p or £0.70

7. 79

8. 12:45 or quarter to one

9. West or W

10. 13

11. 4

12. £5.60 or 560p

13. the right-angled triangle

14. −7°C

15. £2 or £2.00 or two pounds

16. estimate between 64 and 80

17. 8

18. 40

19. 0.1

20. 95

The test score is out of a maximum of 45 marks (30 marks for Part A and 15 for Part B).

If your child has scored highly in Part A, he or she can go on to try the harder questions in Part B.

Write your child's scores below:

Mark scored in Part A

Mark scored in Part B

Total

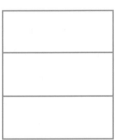

Children at Year 3 may complete a test of this type and from this each child can be levelled and graded according to his or her total score. The Mental Maths Test score is not included when levelling at Year 3.

Total marks 45

Mark	0–9	10–13	14–19	20–26	27–31	32–35	36–39	40–45
Level	Below Level 2	2C	2B	2A	3C	3B	3A	4

If a child scores very highly on the test, there is a possibility of sitting the Year 4 test, to gain clearer information about the extent to which he or she is performing at Level 4.

English at Year 3

Typical seven-year-olds attain Level 2 at the end of Year 2. On average, children progress through one level in two years; this indicates that at the end of Year 3, most children will have attained Level 2 and be working towards Level 3. Some might attain Level 3 and some very able children might attain Level 4.

You can gain an idea of the approximate level at which your child is working by following the conversion tables given on page 58 which show how to convert the marks into a National Curriculum level.

Setting the test

A relaxed approach is best. If you feel anxious, your child will sense this and might not concentrate or perform as well as he or she could.

Work in a quiet place where you and your child will not be distracted.

Your child will need a pencil and, if possible, an eraser; if you do not have an eraser, ask your child to cross out any mistakes made.

Give your child the tests in the order in which they appear in this book. This is important because the tests are linked by a theme. To understand the Writing Test, your child needs to have read the Reading Test. Do *not* ask your child to do all the tests one after the other.

Encourage your child and give praise for what he or she can do. Do not dwell on what he or she *cannot* do but, at another time, you could provide practice in the areas where it is needed. Be guided by your child's teacher as to what are the best ways in which you can help.

To the side of each question is a number indicating how many marks the question is worth, and a circle in which you enter your child's mark.

After each test, add up your child's marks and use the conversion table on page 58 to work out his or her approximate National Curriculum level.

Reading Test

The Reading Test includes:

- a fiction text
- a poem
- an information text.

Setting the tests

Give your child a break between each test.

Allow up to 45 minutes for each Reading Test plus 15 minutes reading time, when no writing is allowed. Your child might not need this long.

At the end of the test enter your child's mark for each question in the circle provided (the number indicates the possible mark).

The answers are on pages 52–53. National Curriculum levels are given on page 58.

Fiction Reading Test

1   Ask your child to turn to the Fiction Reading Test (page 30).

2   Encourage him or her to read the text carefully.

3   Point out that there are two different types of question: those which give a choice of answers, one of which is to be marked by a tick, and those which ask for a written answer. Written answers need not be complete sentences.

4   Do not help your child to read the rest of the text, although you may help with the spelling of the answers. Encourage your child to take care, but point out that he or she may rub out or alter any mistakes made.

5   Tell your child:
   • to find the answers in the text, rather than giving answers which he or she already knows
   • to tick only one box to answer each question
   • to try to answer every question
   • to leave any questions he or she cannot answer, and go back to them at the end
   • to reread the text to find the answers to any questions which he or she has not answered.

6   Allow your child to read the rest of the text independently and to answer the questions without any help.

Poetry Reading Test

Repeat the above for the Poetry Reading Test (page 35).

Information Reading Test

Repeat the above for the Information Reading Test (page 38).

The Parable of the Seeds

Christians believe that Jesus was the son of God. The Bible, their holy book, tells the following story. Similar stories are found in many religions.

On the shore of a lake, a great crowd gathered around Jesus to hear his teaching. It was such a huge crowd that he had to get into a boat and move out onto the water so that the people could see him. There he sat in the boat with the great crowd in front of him on the shore, right down to the water's edge, some with their feet in the water. People at the back were craning their necks to see him and straining their ears to hear his words. He taught them many things that day through parables.

"Listen!" said Jesus, and a hush spread over the crowd. "A sower went out one day to sow seeds. He scattered the seeds onto the land. Some of them landed on the footpath, and the birds ate them. Other seeds fell on to rocky ground, where the soil was shallow. Those seeds soon sprouted, but their roots were not strong. The sun shone and scorched the shoots. They withered and died because they had poor roots. Some seeds landed among thistles, which grew quickly. Their strong stems and large, prickly leaves choked the seedlings. The seedlings died."

The crowd was still and silent as Jesus finished the parable: "But some of the seeds fell onto good soil. They grew strong and produced a fine crop of corn with thirty ... sixty ... even a hundred times as many seeds."

Jesus paused and said, "If you have ears to hear, then hear."

Afterwards, when the crowd had gone, Jesus' followers asked him why he spoke to people in parables. He answered, "*You* have been given the secret of the kingdom of God, but *others* need parables to help them to find it. Without help, they might look and look for it but see nothing. They might hear and hear, but understand nothing. With help, they can turn to God and be forgiven."

Jesus explained the parable. "The seed is the word of God. The sower is sowing the word of God. The seed which lands on the footpath is the word of God. The people there hear it but soon forget it.

"The seed which lands on the rocky ground is the word of God. The people there hear it with joy, but it is the same with them — it finds no roots in them. They are eager to believe, but if they meet trouble because of their belief, they give it up.

"The seed which falls into the thistles is the word of God. The people there believe, but they are too fond of worldly things: money and glamour and things which can be bought. The word is choked out of their lives.

"The seed which finds the good soil is the word of God. People there hear the word and welcome it. They believe and their belief grows thirty ... sixty ... even a hundredfold."

Tick the correct answer.

1 The seeds which landed on the rocky ground

| were eaten by birds | were scorched by the sun | were choked by the weeds | grew strong shoots |

2 Jesus sat in a boat because

| there was a flood | he wanted to cross the lake | there were no seats | the people could not see him |

3 Some of the corn seedlings were choked by

| thistles | grass | trees | water plants |

4 In the parable, Jesus used the seed to stand for

| people | himself | gold | the word of God |

5 Which two examples of worldly things were given in the parable?

| gold | money | glamour | jewellery |

6 Jesus told his followers that he taught through parables because

| they helped people to find the kingdom of God | he liked telling stories | he didn't want to bore people | the parables were the word of God |

1

1

1

1

2

1

TOTAL

7

7 What happened to the seeds which landed on the footpath?

_____

_____

1

8 What did Jesus say people might do if no one helped them to find the kingdom of God?

_____

_____

2

9 Name the four places in which the sower's seeds landed.

_____

_____

_____

_____

4

10 When Jesus explained the parable, what did he say the sower was sowing?

_____

_____

1

11 Which people did Jesus say soon forgot the word of God?

_____

_____

1

12 What made the people on the rocky ground give up their belief?

_____

_____

1

TOTAL

10

13 What made the people of the thistles forget the word of God?

_____

_____

1

14 Which words tell you that the people listening to Jesus were eager to hear what he had to say?

_____

_____

2

15 Which words tell you that the people became very quiet when Jesus spoke?

_____

_____

_____

2

16 What question did Jesus' followers ask him?

_____

_____

1

17 Jesus said that people can turn to God and be forgiven. For what might they be forgiven?

_____

_____

_____

TOTAL

8

A Spike of Green

When I went out

The sun was hot,

It shone upon

My flower pot.

And there I saw

A spike of green

That no one else

Had ever seen!

On other days

The things I see

Are mostly old

Except for me.

But this green spike

So new and small

Had never yet

Been seen at all!

Barbara Baker

Tick the correct answers for questions 1–5.

1 What was the weather like?

cold	freezing	hot	cool

2 On what did the sun shine?

a stone	a garden	a house	a flower pot

3 In the poem, which word rhymes with green?

grain	grew	seen	me

4 What was the green spike?

the point of a garden tool	the first shoot of a new plant	a point on a green fence	a garden cane

5 What made the spike special?

no one else had seen it	it was green	the sun made it grow	it was in a plant pot

6 Was the poet young or old?

_____

How can you tell?

_____

_____

1

1

1

1

1

2

TOTAL

7

36

7 Who had planted the seed or bulb from which the green spike grew?

_____

Which words tell you this?

_____

2

8 What feeling is the poet trying to show?

_____

_____

What makes you think this?

_____

_____

2

9 Did you enjoy this poem?

_____

Give your reasons.

_____

_____

_____

_____

_____

_____

_____

_____

3

TOTAL

7

Seeds

Flowering plants grow seeds in order to produce young plants. The seeds have different ways of travelling away from the parent plant. They need to travel so that all the seeds from one plant do not grow close together and become overcrowded.

Exploding seed pods
In some plants, such as the poppy, columbine, meadow cranesbill and pea, the seeds are in seed pods which dry out. They explode and scatter the seeds in all directions.

Poppy

Flying seeds
A dandelion 'clock' is a soft, white ball of tiny, light seeds on stalks. They are so light that a puff of wind can blow them away. Thistledown, the seeds of the thistle, are also scattered by the wind.

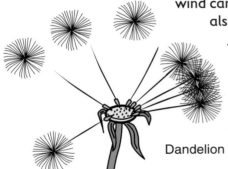

Dandelion

The shapes of seeds can help them to fly away from the parent plant. 'Aeroplanes' or 'helicopters' from the sycamore tree, and 'ash keys' from the ash tree, spin in the air.

Floating seeds
Seeds which float can be carried by streams and rivers. The coconut, a giant seed from the coconut palm, floats because it is hollow. The pod of the sea rocket also floats because it is hollow. Some seeds have a flat shape which helps them to float (for example, the seeds of the lotus plant).

Seeds spread by animals
There are two main ways in which animals can help to scatter seeds. Birds and other animals eat rowan berries, blackberries, bilberries and other fruits. The fruit is digested but the seeds pass through their bodies. They might travel, inside the bird, far from the parent plant.

Some seeds grow inside pods called 'burrs' with tiny hooks on them. The burrs cling to an animal's fur and travel with the animal until they are rubbed or shaken off. A Swiss scientist named Georges de Mestral noticed burrs from burdock clinging to his dog's coat by their tiny hooks (or barbs), and saw that the same idea could be used for a fastening – he invented Velcro!

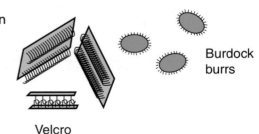

Burdock burrs

Velcro

Tick the correct answer for questions 1–6.

1 Why do plants produce seeds?

| to make flowers | to make leaves | to make new plants | to provide food for birds |

1

2 Why would it be bad for the new young plants if the seeds could not move away from the parent plant?

| they would become overcrowded | they would look untidy | gardeners would pull them up as weeds | animals would eat them |

1

3 Which of these plants has seeds which float?

| poppy | dandelion | lotus | burdock |

1

4 Which two of these words describe the seed of the dandelion?

| hollow | light | winged | tiny |

1

5 What name is given to a seed pod with tiny hooks on it?

| key | burr | helicopter | clock |

1

6 Which plant helped Georges de Mestral to invent Velcro?

| burdock | thistle | dandelion | coconut |

1

7 How do the seeds of the meadow cranesbill and columbine travel?

_____

_____

_____

1

TOTAL

7

39

8 Which tree has seeds called 'keys'?

_____

1

9 Which two characteristics of seeds help them to float?

_____

_____

_____

2

10 Does a bird help or harm a plant when it eats its berries?

_____

2

Explain your answer.

_____

_____

_____

11 Describe how seed pods gave Georges de Mestral the idea of inventing Velcro. Use up to 25 words.

_____

_____

_____

_____

_____

_____

_____

3

TOTAL

8

At Key Stage 2 children's writing is assessed through two Writing Tests:

- a Longer Writing Test (45 minutes)
- a Shorter Writing Test (20 minutes).

Schools will be told what type of writing tasks to set but the topic is up to the teacher, who will take into account the interest and experience of the class. One Writing Test will be based on fiction and the other on non-fiction.

Children should be allowed time to plan their writing for both tasks, which they should not do one after the other.

The Longer Writing Test is assessed for: **Sentence structure and punctuation** (up to eight marks), **Text structure and organisation** (up to eight marks) and **Composition and effect** (up to 12 marks). (Total 28 marks.)

Sentence structure and punctuation focuses on the use of variation of types of sentence, clarity, purpose and effect, and on grammatical accuracy and punctuation.

Text structure and organisation focuses on organising and presenting whole texts effectively, sequencing and structuring information, ideas and events, constructing paragraphs and using cohesion within and between paragraphs.

Composition and effect focuses on imaginative, interesting and thoughtful writing, writing a text which is suitable for its purpose and for the reader, and organising and presenting a text effectively.

The Shorter Writing Test is assessed for: **Sentence structure, punctuation and text organisation** (up to four marks) and **Composition and effect** (up to eight marks). (Total 12 marks.)

In National Tests **Handwriting** is assessed in the longer task (three marks), but it is not assessed in the tests in this book.

Spelling is assessed in a separate test (seven marks for a 20-word test).

The mark schemes each year are specific to the tests; new level thresholds are set for each year's tests to ensure that standards are maintained each year.

The conversion charts to National Curriculum levels provided at the end of this book should be regarded as a rough guide only.

This test helps you to gain an insight into your child's ability to write independently: to communicate meaning to the reader using punctuation, spelling and handwriting.

Writing Test

Sheets of lined paper are provided on pages 45–46 and 48–49 for your child to write on.

Your child should first have read the passages in the Reading Tests.

Allow 45 minutes for the longer Writing Test and 20 minutes for the Shorter Writing Test.

The guide to marking your child's Writing Test can be found on pages 54–56.

An indication of National Curriculum levels is given on page 58.

Longer Writing Test

1   Give your child the planning sheet on page 44.

2   Read the starting point aloud.

3   Discuss the points on page 43 but you must not tell your child what to write!

4   Point out that grammar, spelling and punctuation are important.

5   Remind your child to think about punctuation and how it helps the reader to make sense of what is written.

6   If your child finishes the test before 45 minutes are up, encourage him or her to read it through to look for anything which can be improved and to check grammar, spelling and punctuation.

Shorter Writing Test

1   Reread the Information Reading Test on page 38 with your child.

2   Give your child the planning sheet (page 47).

3   Read the instructions with him or her.

4   Talk about the key features of a news report, ensuring that he or she knows the meanings of all the terms used.

5   Tell him or her to think about how to organise the report so that it is easy to follow.

6   Remind your child to think about punctuation and how it helps the reader to make sense of what is written.

7   If your child finishes the test before 20 minutes are up, encourage him or her to read it through to look for anything which can be improved and to check grammar, spelling and punctuation.

Read *The Parable of the Seeds*.

The story is from about two thousand years ago in the area where Israel is now. The people were from farming communities.

Rewrite the parable with a modern setting and in a place you know.

Instead of seeds landing on the ground, your parable could be about:

- eggs laid by hens
- caterpillars hatching into butterflies
- gas balloons set off at a fair and landing in different places
- or something else which interests you.

Before you write your parable, you need to plan it.
Make some very brief notes on the planning sheet on the next page.

Planning sheet

Setting	Audience

When does it happen? Where?

Who are the people who will listen to the parable? What kinds of things interest them?

Main events

Make notes about what happens in the parable.

Explanation

What does the parable teach?

TOTAL

28

Planning sheet

Write a news report about a giant seed which has been found somewhere near where you live.

Plan your work before you begin writing.

You should think about:

- a headline (you could leave this until last)
- the information you are going to give the readers
- how to split your report into paragraphs
- an interesting opening
- how to keep the readers' attention
- how you will end the report.

Your report should be short. It has to fit into a very small space on the page of the newspaper.

48

49

TOTAL

12

49

Spelling Test

This test contains words which are generally known by eight-year-olds; they include many of the spelling strategies suggested for Year 3 in the National Literacy Strategy *Framework for Teaching*.

The Spelling test is a short passage with words missed out.

Cut out the text on page 57.

The words in bold are the missing words. You should read aloud from this text.

Your child should write in the test copy on page 51.

Allow 10 minutes.

At the end of the test, give a mark for each correct word.

National Curriculum levels are given on page 58.

This Spelling Test, of 20 words, is marked out of 20. In the National Test for English the Spelling Test consists of 20 words but carries only seven marks.

1   Ask your child to look at his or her copy of the text (page 51). Show him or her that some of the words have been left out.

2   Ask your child to listen to you reading the complete text.

3   Tell your child that you are going to read the text again and that he or she should write in the missing words as you read.

4   Read the text aloud again, pausing after each missing word, to give your child time to write it on the test copy.

You can repeat each of the missing words up to three times.

"_____!" said Jesus, and a _____

spread over the crowd. "A sower went out one day to sow

seeds. He _____ the seeds onto the land.

Some of them landed on the _____, and the birds

_____ them. Other seeds fell onto rocky

_____, where the soil was _____.

_____ seeds soon _____, but their

roots were not strong. The sun _____ and

scorched the shoots. They withered and died

_____ they had poor roots. Some seeds landed

among _____, which grew _____.

Their strong stems and large, _____ leaves

_____ the seedlings. The seedlings died."

The crowd was _____ and silent as Jesus finished

the parable: "But some of the seeds fell onto good soil.

They grew strong and produced a fine crop of

_____ with_____ ... sixty ... even a

_____ times as_____ seeds."

Answers

Reading Test

Question number	Answer	Mark	Parent's notes and additional information
The Parable of the Seeds			
1	were scorched by the sun	1	
2	the people could not see him	1	
3	thistles	1	
4	the word of God	1	
5	money and glamour	2	
6	they helped people to find the kingdom of God	1	
7	birds ate them	1	
8	They might look and look but see nothing, and hear and hear but understand nothing.	2	Your child should include both parts of the sentence.
9	the footpath, rocky ground, among thistles and on good soil	4	
10	the word of God	1	
11	those on the footpath	1	
12	meeting with trouble because of their belief	1	
13	worldly things	1	
14	'craning their necks' and 'straining their ears'	2	1 mark for each
15	'a hush spread over the crowd'	2	1 mark for just 'hush' and another if the complete answer is given.
16	Why do you speak in parables?	1	
17	for things they have done wrong. *or* for their sins	2	Accept any answer which shows that the child understands the word 'forgiven', *not necessarily in a Christian sense.*
Poetry Reading Test			
1	hot	1	
2	a flower pot	1	
3	seen	1	
4	the first shoot of a new plant	1	
5	no one else had seen it	1	

Question number	Answer	Mark	Parent's notes and additional information
6	young It says 'The things I see/Are mostly old/Except for me'.	2	1 mark for each part of the answer
7	the poet herself 'My flower pot'	2	1 mark for each
8	excitement (about something special) The exclamation marks make it sound exciting *or* The poet compares the new shoot with the old things he or she usually sees *or* The poet repeats that the shoot had never been seen: 'That no one else/Had ever seen' and 'Had never yet been seen at all'.	2	1 mark for naming the feeling. 1 mark for saying what made your child think that in a convincing way.
9	personal evaluation and justification	3	Base the mark on the number and quality of reasons given for liking or disliking the poem. Children should be able to explain their responses clearly.

Information Reading Test

Question number	Answer	Mark	Parent's notes and additional information
1	to make new plants	1	
2	they would become overcrowded	1	
3	lotus	1	
4	light, tiny	1	Both answers needed
5	burr	1	
6	burdock	1	
7	Their seed pods explode and scatter the seeds.	1	
8	ash	1	
9	being hollow and having a flat shape	2	1 mark for each
10	It helps it. The bird digests the berries but not the seeds. They pass through its body without being harmed. The bird helps the plant to spread its seeds.	2	The key point is that your child understands that animals are beneficial to plants.
11	The description should include: burrs from a burdock plant clung on to his dog's coat; he noticed their little hooks; he made a fastener which worked in the same way.	3	1 mark for each – maximum 3 marks

Longer Test

Sentence structure and punctuation	Marks
Uses some simple sentences, often short and beginning with the subject and the verb: for example, *Some of the balloons landed in gardens, Some balloons burst.* There ` might be some incomplete sentences. Uses capital letters to begin sentences and full stops to end them.	1
Makes some connections between sentences: for example, by using pronouns which refer back to people and objects already mentioned (*he, it, she, they*). Uses mainly *and, but* and *then* to join parts of sentences, but sometimes uses *or* and *if*. Begins sentences with capital letters and ends them with full stops, and might use exclamation marks and question marks, as appropriate.	2–3
Uses mainly simple grammatically accurate statements in the past tense. In some sentences there is repetition of subjects and verbs: for example, *The balloons landed on the road and the balloons burst.* Uses simple adjectives to describe places: *a bumpy field, a lovely garden, a busy road.* Verbs agree with their subjects: for example, *I was, you were, it was, they were.* Uses exclamation marks and question marks, as appropriate. Uses some speech marks to punctuate dialogue, although not always accurately.	4–5
Uses simple and compound sentences in the past tense, joining clauses and phrases with a range of connective words such as *and, because, but, so, then, though, while.* Uses words which signal time sequences: *after that, meanwhile, next, then.* Uses speech marks to punctuate dialogue.	6–7
Uses simple, compound and complex sentences with clauses linked by a range of connective words and phrases such as *and, but, which*: for example, *Some children found the balloons which landed in the garden.* Writes consistently in the third person (*he/she, it, they*). Uses some commas to mark phrases or clauses where appropriate.	8

Text structure and organisation	Marks
Makes some connection between ideas and links some events in single sentences.	1
Gives a simple recount with a brief sequence of events, roughly in the correct order. Opens the writing with a sentence indicating setting (time or place or both).	2–3
Writes in a way which maintains the recount of events in the correct order; explains some of the events and ends with a suitable conclusion, rather than 'leaving the story hanging'. Sometimes begins separate sections or paragraphs.	4–5
Gives an introduction. The writing shows evidence of planning around the main points, using the passage as a model. The conclusion explains the parable.	6–7
The main points are recounted in separate paragraphs and there is a concluding explanatory paragraph relating the events in the story to the words of God, as in the original.	8

Composition and effect	
Uses simple vocabulary connected with the topic: for example, *balloons, came down, gas, went up.*	1–2
Uses more detailed vocabulary appropriate to the topic: for example, *floated, landed, scattered.*	3–5
Makes an attempt to create interest or expectation. Gives details about people, events or places: for example, *The balloons floated up into the sky, bobbing this way and that.* Selects some useful vocabulary to express detail: for example, *brightly-coloured, bobbing this way and that.* Introduces speech where appropriate.	6–8
Uses a style which is suitable for the type of writing and for the audience, and is maintained for most of the writing. Creates the atmosphere of the scene through using language to describe the response of the audience: for example, *The crowd was still and silent, The men were restless and muttered to one another.*	9–11
The tone of the writing is maintained throughout the parable and is appropriate for the narrator. Uses expressive language such as *craning their necks, straining their ears.*	12

Shorter Test

Sentence structure, punctuation and text organisation	Marks
Description	
Mainly simple grammatically accurate statements in the present tense usually starting with the third person: for example, *They found a giant seed.* Joins some clauses with *and*, sometimes with repetition: for example, *They saw the seed and they thought it was a big rock but it was not there yesterday.* Uses other connectives to link simple ideas: for example, *if, so.* Sometimes ends sentences with a full stop and begins them with a capital letter.	1
Uses the third person consistently. Writes some compound sentences, with clauses linked by connectives such as *and*, *but* and *so*. Varies the sentence structure sometimes to support explanation or reasoning: for example, *He knew that it was a seed and not a rock because he could see a root on it.* Uses simple adjectives such as *giant, huge, long.* Uses full stops, capital letters, exclamation marks and question marks – mainly accurately. Might use commas in lists.	2
Uses grammatically accurate clauses. Repetition is used for emphasis.	3
Varies the sentence lengths and uses exclamation marks and question marks where appropriate.	4
Composition and effect	
Writes in a way which communicates some recognisable information: for example, simple statements (which might not be related to one another). Chooses words related to the topic: for example, *grow, plant, seed.*	1
Gives a short series of informative points with some of the ideas grouped into sequences of sentences. Sometimes the layout helps to split ideas into groups (for example, starting on a new line).	2–3
Includes a range of relevant information, in which some parts are grouped by topic, but this grouping might not be consistent. Indicates some divisions between sections of the content: for example, by using headings, line breaks or paragraphing. Suggests a point of view: for example, focusing on how to 'trick' the audience. Uses information suitable for general readers; might use precise word choices drawing on the technical vocabulary of the topic: for example, *barbs, wings.*	4–5
Introduces the topic in an interesting way and makes an attempt to maintain the interest of the reader: for example, through the use of humour or emphasis.	6–7
Introduces an opinion or point of view: for example, *Did it come from outer space? Scientists have never seen anything like it.*	8

"**Listen!**" said Jesus, and a **hush** spread over the crowd. "A sower went out one day to sow seeds. He **scattered** the seeds onto the land. Some of them landed on the **footpath**, and the birds **ate** them. Other seeds fell onto rocky **ground**, where the soil was **shallow**. **Those** seeds soon **sprouted**, but their roots were not strong. The sun **shone** and scorched the shoots. They withered and died **because** they had poor roots. Some seeds landed among **thistles**, which grew **quickly**. Their strong stems and large, **prickly** leaves **choked** the seedlings. The seedlings died."

The crowd was **still** and silent as Jesus finished the parable: "But some of the seeds fell onto good soil. They grew strong and produced a fine crop of **corn** with **thirty** ... sixty ... even a **hundred** times as **many** seeds."

Award 1 mark per correct word.
20 marks in total

National Curriculum Levels

English

Use the conversion tables below to gain an idea of your child's National Curriculum level.

Fiction Reading		Poetry Reading	
Mark	**Level**	**Mark**	**Level**
0–4	Below Level 2	0–3	Below Level 2
5–12	Level 2	4–7	Level 2
13–22	Level 3	8–11	Level 3
23–25	Level 4+	12–14	Level 4+

Information Reading		Spelling	
0–4	Below Level 2	0–3	Below Level 2
5–8	Level 2	4–10	Level 2
9–13	Level 3	11–18	Level 3
14–15	Level 4+	19–20	Level 4+

Writing

Write your child's marks here:

Longer Test	
Shorter Test	
Spelling	
Total	

Writing and Spelling: Approximate National Curriculum Levels

Marks	0–9	10–27	28–53	54–60
Level	Below Level 2	2	3	4